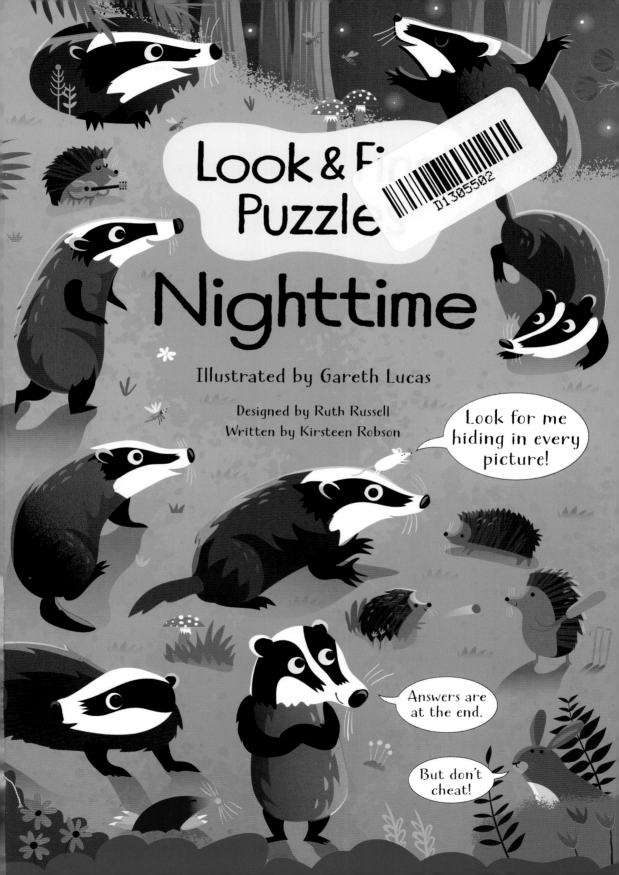

another
3 padlocks

5 more black
spiders

1 other
plane

Have you seen my flashlight?

Spot two sleeping koalas.

Can you find...

3 more green frogs

another 2 rocks

4

5 more
yellow butterflies

a sleeping
joey like this

another
3 snakes

Can you see three more moles like me?

Who's playing the guitar?

Can you find...

another midnight snack

2 more hairbrushes

another
3 combs

3 more spotted
toadstools

a squirrel
just like this

another 3 pink
spiders

2 more
caterpillars

another plate
of pizza

Who's holding a flower?

Can you find...   another upside-down mouse   3 more snails, all different

10

Which leopard has lost her spots?

Can you find...

2 other fishing frogs

6 more floating candles

another 2
fish like this

5 more
dragonflies

another little
yellow bird

3 more of
these birds

a toy just like
this one

3 more
orange flags

Find two cubs underneath their mother.

Can you find...

another 4 squirrels

2 more lanterns

Have you seen my blue clock?

Who is wearing red headphones?

Can you find...   3 more buckets   another 2 of these

18

3 more plants
like this

5 more
white flowers

another centipede
like this

19

Can you find...   another 3 slices   4 more
                                   of cake   bumblebees

Can you find a teapot for our tea party?

a pink ribbon just like this

5 more blue stars

another 2 cups and saucers

another 3
pink striped hats

1 more
blue scarf

another bird
like this

Can you find... 8 more flying white birds 2 other snakes

24

Can you find two cats linking their tails?

Can you find...

3 toy mice like this

6 blue birds, all different

Can you spot a sleeping bird?

Who's cuddling a teddy bear?

Can you find...

another 5 yellow eye masks

3 more purple bats

6 snails
like this

3 caterpillars,
all different

3 more
bananas

Answers

Cover

2-3

4-5

6-7

8-9

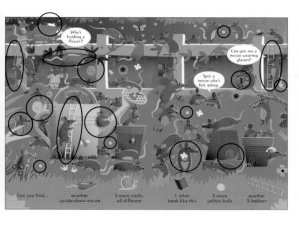

10–11

12–13

14–15

16–17

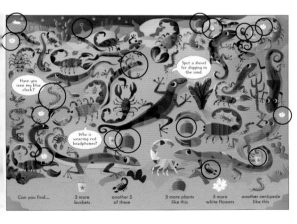

18–19

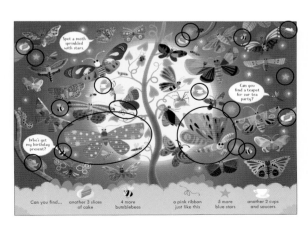

20–21

22–23

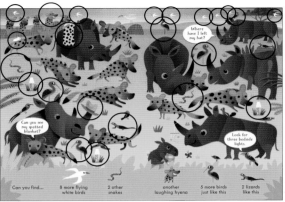

24–25

26–27

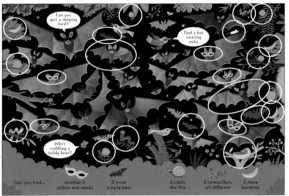

28–29

First published in 2021 by Usborne Publishing Ltd, Usborne House, 83-85 Saffron Hill, London, EC1N 8RT, England. usborne.com ©2021 Usborne Publishing Ltd. The name Usborne and the Balloon logos are trade marks of Usborne Publishing Ltd. All rights reserved. No part of this publication may be reproduced, stored in a retrieval system, or transmitted in any form or by any means without the prior permission of Usborne Publishing Ltd. First published in America in 2021, UE, EDC, Tulsa, Oklahoma 74146, usbornebooksandmore.com Printed in China.